Wild Flowers

Engravings by Redouté, Besler and several artists
Texts by Matthias Hermann
Translated by Grace Jackman

GALAHAD BOOKS • NEW YORK CITY

We know that the great Swiss-French writer Jean-Jacques Rousseau, disillusioned by the difficulties of life in society became an amateur botanist which seems to have given him considerable consolation. He explained this in his famous *Reveries of a Solitary Walker*, describing his stay on a small wild island in the Lake of Bienne (Switzerland):

THE HAPPINESS OF A PLANT-LOVER *(according to Jean-Jacques Rousseau)*

"Since I no longer wanted to work, I had to have some amusement which would keep me occupied without effort, in short, one suited to a lazy person. I undertook to do the Flora petrinsularis and to describe all the plants on the island without exception, in sufficient detail to keep me busy the rest of my days. It is said that a German has written a book about lemon peel, I should have done one on every grass of the fields, every moss in the woods, every lichen on the rocks; I did not want to let a blade of grass escape me, not one plant atom but must be fully described. Because of this fine project, every morning after lunch, which we all took together, I went, magnifying glass in hand an with the Systema naturae under my arm, to visit some canton of the island which I had for this purpose divided into small squares with the intention of going through them one after the other in every season. There is nothing more extraordinary than the pleasure, bordering on ecstasy, that I experienced with every observation on the structure and organisation of plants, on the role of the sexual organs in fructification, the system of which was quite new to me at that time. The distinction of generic characteristics of which I had not the slightest idea beforehand proved a source of delight as I checked them on the common species waiting to find rarer ones. The forking of two long stamens in Prunella of Self-heal, the spring of those in the Nettle and the Wall-pellitory, the explosion of the balsam fruit and the box-tree capsule, a thousand little games in fructification that I was observing for the first time and which filled me with joy.".....

"Trees, shrubs and plants are the clothing and adornment of the earth. There is nothing so sad to the eye as a naked stark landscape with only stones, mud and sand. But given life by Nature and dressed like a bride in the middle of water-courses with singing birds, the earth offers Man in the harmony of its three reigns a sight full of life, interest and charm, the only sight in the world of which his eyes and heart never tire.".....

"Bright flowers, the enamel of the fields, fresh shade, streams, woods, greenery, come and purify my imagination. My soul is dead to all great movements and can no longer be touched except by sensitive things; I have only feelings but it is no longer through them that pain or pleasure can reach me here below. Drawn by the smiling objects which surround me, I consider contemplate and compare them, finally learn to classify them, and suddenly I am as much a botanist as anyone need be who wishes to study Nature in order to find constantly new reasons for loving it.

"I do not seek to gain knowledge: it is too late. Besides, I have never noticed that so much knowledge contributed to happiness in life. But I try to find gentle, simple amusements which I can enjoy without difficulty and which distract me from my unhappiness. It costs me no trouble and no effort to wander carelessly from plant to plant, from herb to herb, to examine them, compare their various characteristics, note their relationships and their differences, to observe the organisation of the plant in order to follow the function and the role of these living machines, sometimes successfully to find their general laws, the reason and the purpose of their various structures, to marvel in gratitude at the hand which gave me all this to enjoy.

"The plants seem to have been sown in profusion over the earth, like the stars in the sky to invite man through the attraction of pleasure and curiosity to study nature; but the stars are very far from us, you need some basic knowledge, instruments, machines, or long ladders to reach them and bring them closer to us. Plants however are within our reach. They are born at our feet and in our hands, so to speak, and if the smallness of their essential parts sometimes hides them from us, the instruments making them visible are much more easy to use than those for astronomy. Botany is the study of a solitary, lazy person; a point and a magnifying glass are all the material he needs. He walks, wanders freely from one object to another, reviews every flower with interest and curiosity and as soon as he begins to understand the laws of their structure enjoys watching them with an effortless pleasure as acute as if it had cost him a great deal. This idle occupation holds a charm which is only felt in the total calm of passion, but which alone at that point suffices to make life happy and gentle."...

"This study has become for me a kind of passion filling the void of all those I no longer have."

IN SEARCH OF WILD FLOWERS

Of all the places a botanist must explore, old walls are one of the most picturesque. They should mainly be visited early in spring. Ruined walls, particularly those which have surrounded or do still surround private gardens in which for use or ornamentation local or foreign plants had been cultivated, frequently become a new breeding ground for some of them which develop and reproduce as well as in their natural region.

The fields offer the botanist elegantly-shaped flora, in cultivated land as such, annual plants whose total development takes the same time as that for cultivated plants, cereals or others.

The best time for exploring the fields is about one month or six week before harvesting; then a whole legion of plants are in flower, the Cornflower, Corn Poppy, Larkspur, Melampyrum

or Cow-wheat, whose origins would be hard to prove. In June too, the botanist can gather several cruciferae and umbelliferae, and almost all the annual speedwells.

Vines offer annual species particularly the Fumaria, Calendula arvensis, and so on. Depending on the nature of the ground and particularly the position of the vines, there sometimes appear plants of a slightly more meridional climate.

The most richly wooded areas are, of course, those where the various species are comparatively small, thinly scattered and also where the ground is fresh or damp rather than sandy and dry. Woods formed exclusively of resinous trees harbor generally poor vegetation in terms of species and sickly in terms of individual plants.

Forests offer a considerable number of plants belonging to almost all the broad divisions of the plant world. Such diversity obviously involves differences in the flowering-time. The botanist must go out from November to March to find the liverworts and the lichens; in April he can gather primroses, snowdrops and wood anemones.

Heathland is generally so poor that these shrubs are almost the only vegetation.

For the botanist it is a strange feeling to glance at the very characteristic vegetation near dwellings. This flora is quite small and the species seems to seek out the best position rather than a certain quantity of humus or saline substances in the soil. This is the case of the Nettle.

Flora in flooded places depends on the depth of the water. It is usually more luxuriant and varied if the water is not very deep. It consists of a variety of elegant flowers, changing according to whether the water is still or running.

The vegetation of swamps wich is closely related to the last-mentioned, is one of the best characterised. It belongs almost exclusively to the gramineae and cyperaceae. June to July is the best period for exploring this flora.

The botanist may, on scouring the plain, be struck by the fact that several herbaceous plants in the flora have very developed stems and leaves while their roots are generally slender and he would note that the inverse was true in very tall plants. Usually stems and leaves rarely exceed 4"; the roots on the contrary penetrate the fissures or moving debris of rocks often to a considerable depth. The foliage of plants on the plain is soft and drooping while that of Alpine plants is generally covered with a viscous substance.

In the mountains the botanist is assured of varied and abundant finds, the better the higher he goes. Grassy places where torrents meet as they flow down from the heights must be explored with care; they are usually the habitat of a certain number of rare species belonging in particular to the sedge and rush families. The rocky parts known as gravel or scree are of great interest to the explorer; there the often finds a good number of species of the highest and most inaccessible peaks which are better developed and easier to gather and which have been brought down in various ways, particularly in melting snows.

The best time for plant-finding in the mountains is May to June for the lowlands, mid-July between 3,000'-6,000' and end July to mid-August for the upper regions. Plants in meridional regions have common characteristics: slender roots, narrow leaves sometimes rather leathery with an often penetrating odour. The amateur should explore these regions for preference between March and June and in September.

The botanist finds the greatest variety of flowers in hedgerows and along country lanes what is more by the law of alternance there are rich pickings for a good part of the year.

Absinthium
Common Wormwood

Common Wormwood or Absinth is a perennial herb with a woody rootstock and leaves 2- or 3-pinnate; the flower heads are globose, yellow, borne in short axillary spikes forming slender leafy panicles 6"-18" long. It is found in arid uncultivated land in continental and meridional regions. It flowers in July and August. The leaves yield an alcoholic extract soluble in alcohol which is a tonic and stimulant in small doses, but produces giddiness and inebriation if taken in quantity *(A)*.

Actaea
Baneberry

This is a small genus of herbaceous perennials. They have two or three ternate leaves and racemes of small whitish flowers. The fruit itself is a many-seeded berry. *Actaea spicata* has a shining black berry while *Actaea rubra* has a red fruit. These plants are found in woods, hedgerows and shady mountainous places. They are very purgative and Linnaeus, the renowned Swedish botanist, states that the berries are poisonous, killing dogs and giving men high fever—hence their name, Baneberry *(B)*.

(B)

(B)

14

(A)

Adonis

Pheasant's eye

There are about twenty species of annual or perennial herbs. Each consists of alternate leaves divided into linear segments with showy solitary terminal flowers. *Adonis aestivalis,* roughly 12" high, is an annual with a simple stem branching at the top only with crimson flowers. Some contain an abundance of acrid juice which is dangerous, but the famous Dr. Parkinson said that an infusion made from seeds was effective against colic *(A)*.

Agropyrum repens

Couchgrass

The stems, between 2' and 3' high are erect, cylindrical and articulate, bearing alternate leaves, which are pubescent above, glabrous below, and slightly grey-green in color. The flowers are small and greenish, clustered in four or five small, alternate wide-spaced spikes, together making up one long loose terminal spike. Couchgrass is very common in uncultivated ground, scrubland and ill-kempt fields. It seems its leaves are a good purgative for dogs *(B)*.

(B)   *(A)*

(A)

Agrimonia
Agrimony

Members of the rose family, there are herbaceous perennials with unequal pinnate leaves and long spikes of yellow flowers. The leaflets are toothed, hairy, and oblong-eliptical to oval in shape. They were one time considered to be of medicinal value; the rootstock is astringent, yielding a yellow dye. They are found in dry places, pasture-land, hedgerows and shrubs. *Agrimonia odorata* which grows to between 2' and 3' high prefers woody and shady, damp places *(A)*.

Ajuga
Bugle

There are about thirty species of annual or perennial herbs in this genus. *Ajuga reptans* is a small plant with green leaves, sometimes spotted with red, which diminish in size from the base to the top of the plant. It's flowers are bluish in color and form a whorling pyramidal spike. There are white and yellow-flowered varieties *(B)*.

(B)   *(B)*   *(B)*

(A)

Allium
Garlic

This covers about 280 species of bulbous plants growing mostly in the temperate regions of the northern hemisphere. *Alium sativum* is garlic and grows from 1' to 2' high, with either a straight or twisted stem. The leaves are linear and acute; and the flowers are white, tinged red or greenish, and the umbels bear bulbils. The bulb has oblong ovate offsets which provide the cloves of garlic used in the kitchen. The Athenians were great garlic eaters, the Romans believed it warded off evil, and as anyone who has seen *Dracula* knows it is usefull for keeping vampires at bay *(A)*.

Anagalis arvensis
Pimpernel

Pimpernel or « Poor Man's Weatherglass » is an annual prostrate herb, the stem is four-angled, the leaves are ovate and spread in opposites or in threes. The flower color is variable—red, blue or white *(B)*.

(A)   *(A)*   *(A)*

(A)   *(A)*   *(B)*

Andromeda

Marsh rosemary

These are low, evergreen, diffuse or compact shrubs with leaves linear-lance-shaped, tapering to both ends, with flowers pendent. They are found in both arctic and temperate regions of the northern hemisphere. *Andromeda arborea* is the sorrel tree. *Andromeda polifolia,* crystal tea, or wild rosemary, is one that can be used to make refreshing decoctions *(A)*.

Anemone nemorosa

Wood anemone

Wood anemone is one of the main species of anemone, some of which have become garden flowers. This plant is related to *anemone sylvestris* the snowdrop windflower. Wood anemone grows about 6" high from a horizontal slender rootstock. The leaves are deeply toothed, lance-shaped, acute and ternate. The flowers are generally white, often tinged with rose on the outside. The scapes are one-flowered. It contains an acrid volatile substance and an acid. It is an irritant, but is used to produce distilled water for the perfume trade *(B)*.

Angelica

Holy ghost

Angelica is usually a perennial plant, stout and tall, consisting of compound leaves with large segments and multi-rayed compound umbels of small white or purplish flowers. Depending on the species, these plants grow to between 2' and 5' in height. The blanched mid-ribs of the leaves can be used like celery, the leaf stalks are used for flavoring, the root is eaten as a vegetable, and the fruits are used for flavoring and perfumery. The Laps chew is much as pioneers chewed tobacco *(C)*.

(B)   *(C)*

(A)

Anthirrinium majus

Snapdragon

This is a perennial usually branched from the base of the stem. It grows 9" to 45" high; the leaves are oblong and lance-shaped, and the flowers grow in close racemes and the colors vary from white, yellow, pink, orange, crimson, and carmen to magenta *(A)*.

Anthyllis vulneraria

Lady's fingers

This is an herbaceous tufted perennial, 6" to 16" high, with leaflets in two to six pairs, narrow and oblong in shape. The flowers are yellow, white, red or pinkish in color and grow in crowded—usually twin—heads. It is also known as woundwort and in bygone times, countryfolk used to make poultices from it. It has long been used freely in Germany for feeding horses and dairy cows *(B)*.

Arctium

Burdock

Common Burdock or *Arctium minus* is a biennial or perennial plant with a long fleshy rootstock—white within, brown without—and a cylindrical, erect stem, reddish in color, growing to 3' or higher with many branches. The leaves are soft, wavy and slightly toothed on the edges, deep green above, white and downy below, and the tubular flowers are purple-violet growing in small flowerheads, together forming a kind of terminal panicle. It grows in uncultivated places and among rubbish. One edible variety comes from Japan *(C)*.

(A)   *(B)*

(C)

Arctostaphylos
Bearberry

This is a genus of handsome shrubs and small trees. *Arctostaphylos Uva-ursi,* or Bearberry, is a prostrate rapidly spreading shrub, rooting at the nodes. The flowers grow in small pendent terminal racemes and are pinkish in color. The leaves are obovate or oval and smooth on both sides. The fruit is brilliant red, globose and smooth. It was for some centuries cultivated for medical purposes. In Greece, the leaves and bark were used for tanning hides. The fruits have been used, particularly in Italy and Spain, to make *eau-de-vie (A).*

Aristolochia
Birthwort

This genus got its name because some species were thought to ease childbirth. *Aristolochia serpentaria* or Virginia Snake Root is a deciduous trailer. The flowers are three-lobed and greenish, shaped rather like the letter 'S', and grow from near the base of the stem on bracteate, spreading peduncles. The roots were long used as a snake bite remedy. *Aristolochia rotunda,* Apple of the Earth, has yellowish flowers, hairy without, striped or dark red within, with an ovate lip. It is a hardy perennial *(B).*

Arnica
Mountain tobacco

This is a genus of about 18 species. *Arnica montana* or common Mountain Tobacco, is a tufted plant about 12" high, with smooth, oblong, lance-shaped basal leaves. The large, radiate yellow flowerheads, with 3 or 4 flowers, measure about 2" across and grow on long peduncles. The plant grows in abundance in the wild, but is rather difficult to cultivate. It is sought after because in the case of shock, a fall, a blow, or violent emotion, this plant rouses and stimulates the nervous functions. It is also useful for bruises and bleeding *(C).*

(C)

(A)

(B)

Artemisia
Artemisia

This is the plant which yields absinth. *Artemisia* is a large genus of shrubs, sub-shrubs and herbaceous perennials, mostly aromatic or bitter. Common Wormwood is an herbaceous perennial with a woody rootstock. The leaves are two or three-pinnate; the flowerheads globose, yellow, borne in short axillary spikes, forming slender leafy panicles 6" to 18" long. An other kind is the *Mugwort*: this plant has a woody rootstock, with reddish stems from 2' to 4' long which are covered with silvery white silky down. The leaves are variable, the flowerheads, purplish or dull yellow, are ovoid and form terminal slender panicles *(A)*.

Astragalus
Milk vetch

This is a genus of roughly 1,200 species, mostly annual or perennial herbs. The flowers are papilionaceous, usually in axillary racemes or spikes. The leaves are usually unequally pinnate, and the flowers violet, purple, yellow or white. The main species come from the East. Theophrastes discovered one on a mountain in Crete. Several yield a gum used for making emulsions. It is interesting to note that many plants with "gala" in their name were used for pasture-land, because they were believed to improve the milk yield *(B)*.

(A)　　　　　　　　　　　　　　*(B)*

Bellis perennis

Common daisy

The Common daisy, also known as *Herb Margaret* or Mary Gowan, is a small perennial plant with a short rootstock. The leaves are numerous, flat on the ground and obovate. It is a slightly hairy plant tapering at the base. The flowerheads grow solitary on a scape 2" to 5" long; there are many white or pink rays which are always female, and the disk of the flower is bright yellow. This plant was once eaten as a salad. It was also pickled in white wine to make a remedy for rheumatism *(A)*.

Briza

Quake grass

Quaking Grass is a genus of about 12 species of perennial grasses. The flowers are loose pinnacles of large showy spikelets. *Briza media* is a perennial growing 1' to 2' high. The panicle of flowers is about 6" long, the spikelets are heart-shaped and usually purplish in color. Sheep are particularly attracted to it *(B)*.

(B)

(A)

Butomus

Flowering rush

This is a monotypic genus.   *Butomus umbellatus* is a handsome perennial growing on the margin of pools or muddy banks, and is quite hardy.   The stems are longer than the leaves, which grow to 2' to 3' in length, and are linear, slender and pointed, bronze-purple when young but turning green later on.   The flowers are rose-pink.   The rootstocks, baked, are still eaten in northern Asia.   The Scandinavians have long used it in their diet *(A)*.

Cannabis

Hemp

This is a tall herb *(cannabis sativa* is an annual growing to 8'), with coarsely toothed gray-green leaflets.   It is cultivated particularly in India for its fiber (hemp), and when the leaves are dried *(Bhashi* and *Gunjah),* they can be smoked or compounded with water; the resin *(Churrus)* from the leaves is even more powerful.   The seed is used as bird seed or poultry feed *(B)*.

Cardamine pratensis

Mayflower

Cuckoo-flower or Lady's Smock is a plant 1' to 1 1/2' high with pinnate leaves and roundish leaflets on basal leaves which are linear or lance-shaped.   The flower color is variable, pale purple to white, and the plant grows in a corymb.   Also known as Meadow Cress it has the same anti-scorbutic properties as cress *(C)*.

(A)   *(C)*

(B)

Cardus
Thistle

This is a genus of about thirty species made up of annual, biennial or perennial herbs. The leaves usually have spiny teeth. The flower heads are sometimes dioecious; the flowers are all tubular; the tube is short and swollen above, oblique, and generally spreads to form a hemispherical head; the colors are red or purple, and occasionally white *(A)*.

Carline
Carline Thistle

There are about twenty species in this genus. The name comes from Charlemagne whose army is said to have been cured of plague by one species of *Carlina.* The roots contain a resinous, bitter acrid substance reputed to be purgative *(B)*.

(A)

(A)

(A)

(B)

Carum Carvi
Caraway

These plants have spindle-shaped roots, a stem 12" to 24" high, they are slender, branched, grooved and hollow. The umbels are irregular and sit on slender flower stalks. The flowers are white, with irregular outer petals which are deeply notched. The fruit is oblong. Both the roots and the seeds are edible—the seeds are used in Germanic countries for certain kinds of bread. The oil extract is used in perfumery *(A)*.

Cercis
Judas Tree

This is a genus of about seven species of deciduous trees and shrubs which are natives of Europe, North America and China. *Cercis Siliquastrum* can grow up to 40' high although it is usually smaller and more shrubby. The shoots and leaves are glabrous; the leaves are roundish, deeply cordate, usually broad and rounded at the end, and are glaucous green in color. The flowers are bright purplish-rose and grow in a tremendous amount of clusters each consisting of three to six flowers. *Cercis occidentalis* is found in California. The flowers are rose-pink and the leaves kidney-shaped *(B)*.

(A)

(B)

Centaurea Cyanus

Cornflower

The cornflower or "bluebottle" is an annual growing up to 3' high. The leaves are linear and entire, although the lower ones are often toothed and cottony. The flower heads are blue, but cultivated varieties cover every shade from white to blue and deep rose; the flowers of the disc are small but the outer flowers are large, spreading and usually brighter. They have involucral scales, greenish or brown. These are natives of the Old World and there are only about three *Centaurea* in North America.

Chrysanthemum Leucanthemum

Ox-eye Daisy

The dog moon or ox-eye daisy flowers from May to September and is commonly found in the wild state. It is a glabrous perennial growing to roughly 2' high. The leaves are oblong, pinnatifid at the base; the lobes are obtuse and stem-clasping; the basal leaves are obovate and stalked. The flower heads are white, with a yellow disc. These plants are found, both in Europe and North America.

Cichorium
Chicory

This is the Egyptian name for about eight species of plants, native to the warm temperate regions of the Old World. The stems are diffusely branched at flowering time. The leaves are rather large and alternate. The flowers—several to many in heads—all ligulate, are of a beautiful clear blue or rose pink. *Cichorium Endivia* or endive is an annual or biennial with a stem 2' to 4' high, branched and grooved. The leaves are large, with many growing at the base, the flower heads are pale blue and rest on axillary peduncles. It is found in India and other oriental countries. *Cichorium Intybus* or chicory succory has thick roots, and a multi-branched stem 2' to 6' high; the flower heads are bright blue, axillary and sessile. Roasted chicory root is certainly nothing like coffee, except that it turns boiling water black and makes it slightly bitter, however, it is often used to replace real coffee (or sometimes a mixture is made). The historians of antiquity affirm that the Egyptians and the Greeks consumed great quantities of chicory which they called "the liver's friend."

Clematis

This is a genus of about 230 species of herbaceous semi-woody and woody plants, mostly climbing. The leaves are opposite and vary in shape. The flowers vary from solitary to paniculate; the fruits *(achenes)* are borne numerously in globose heads. The genus *Atragene* is distinguished by having a ring of petal-like organs between the sepals and the stamens which are usually called "petaloid staminodes" by the botanists.

Convolvulus
Bindweed

There are about 150 species of these annual or perennial prostrate, twining or erect herbs and sub-shrubs. The leaves are alternate, entire, toothed or lobed, lance-shaped, heart-shaped or spear-shaped. Flowers are funnel or bell-shaped, white or pink, pale red or lilac. *Convolvulus Arvensis* or small bindweed has white or pink flowers.

Coronilla

Crown Vetch

These are either shrubs or herbs with flowers in axillary or terminal umbels. The petals have long claws. *Coronilla Emerus* or scorpion senna is a deciduous shrub growing from 5' to 7' high. The flowers are yellow, grouped 2 to 3 on slender axillary stalks. The leaves are reputed to have laxative properties *(A)*.

Cratægus

Hawthorn

This is a genus of small deciduous trees and shrubs. Its leaves are alternate and its flowers are white fading to pink. The fruit or haw contains from 1 to 5 seeds or stones. American may or apple haw is *Cratægus Aestivalis.* Maythorn is a cultivated species *Cratægus Oxyacantha* with pink and scarlet flowers *(B)*.

(B)

(A)

Crocus Sativus

Saffron Crocus

Common saffron is found from Italy to Kurdistan. It has a flower tube 4" long, with a bearded purple throat; the segments are bright lilac, purple toward the base and purple-veined. The stigmas are long, drooping, entire and scarlet, and are the source of the commercial saffron. These plants were cultivated in Palestine at the time of Solomon. They were used in antiquity for dyeing, making perfumes, coloring foodstuffs such as rice and even sprinkling temples and banquet halls *(A)*.

Dancus Carota

Carrot

This is a biennial plant growing 1' to 2' high, with deeply cut, pinnate leaves whose segments are small and rather hairy. The flowers are white and grow in stalked umbels with incurved outer rays and purplish middle flowers. With cultivation, this plant has changed considerably—its root has become fleshy, thick and sugary. Wild, it is found in fields and pasture-land *(B)*.

(B)

(A)

(A)

Daphne
Garland Flower

These are evergreen deciduous shrubs. The leaves are alternate, rarely opposite, and nearly always entire. The inflorescence is terminal or lateral in clusters, racemes or fascicles. *Daphne Gnidium,* spurge flax, is an erect deciduous shrub 2' to 4' high, with red-brown bark, and leaves which are numerous erect and imbricate, and usually lance-shaped. The flowers are fragrant and grow in terminal or sub-terminal clusters consisting of very few flowers each. The fruit, which is used in Siberia to make a mixture for gargling, is small ovoid and red. The bark is used in particular as a remedy for snake bites.

Delphinium

Larkspur

Delphinium Peregrinum is a perennial smooth, hairy plant with an erect stem 12" to 20" high. The lower leaves are 3 to 5 partite, the upper mostly entire. The flowers grow in rather loose racemes, the sepals are blue, occasionally white and hairy without. The upper petals are blue and two-lobed, the lower are yellowish with a straight-standing spur *(A)*.

Echium

Viper's Bugloss

Common viper's bugloss is a biennial, 2' to 4' high, which is often unbranched. The leaves are linear-lance-shaped and bristly hairy. The flowers are purple in the bud, then violet-blue and downy without. They grow in long spikelike racemes with spikelets simple spreading, one variety, very common in Brazil, has a root that dyes everything red. The color extract of another can be used as a cosmetic *(B)*.

Epilobium

Willow Herb

This is a genus of about sixty species of perennial herbs or shrubs whose characteristics include scattered opposite leaves, axillary flowers, arranged in solitary or in terminal spikes. *Epilobium Angustifolium,* French willow or rose bay, is a perennial, growing from 3' to 6' high, which erect stands has a scarcely branched stem and lance-shaped leaves which are wavy and sessile. The flowers are rose and grow in long terminal racemes *(C)*.

(A)   *(C)*

(B)

Erica
Heath

This name comes from the Greek *Eriko* ("I break") so called because of the brittle stems. There are over 500 species of these evergreen shrubs. They grow wild and are much appreciated by sheep and goats when young. The shape of the leaves range from linear to narrow-oblong or lance-shaped; the flowers grow either solitary in leaf axils or in terminal umbels and provide bees with a superabundance of honey. They were once thought to dissolve stones in the bladder. The most beautiful species are the cape heaths from South Africa; one with particularly lovely rich yellow flowers is *Erica Cavendishiana*.

Evonymus

Spindle Tree

These shrubs or small trees are found in North America, Asia and Europe. The leaves are stalked and usually glabrous, the flowers, 4—or 5—partite, grow in axillary cymes; the fruits are usually lobed or winged. The flowers are unattractive, but the plants themselves have good autumn coloring and bear fine in fruit. The pendulous fruit is brightly colored and splits to reveal the orange outer coverings of the seeds. *Euonymus Japonicus* is a beautiful tree generally growing from 10' to 15' but occasionally reaching 25'. The flowers are wide, greenish-white; the fruit is pinkish and the seed coats orange *(A)*.

Fritillaria

Fritillary

There are about eighty species of these bulbous plants. The bulbs of the Old World species are usually tunicated while the North American species are scaly. The stems are unbranched, erect and leafy; the nodding bell-shaped flowers are either solitary or very few at or near the top of the stems. *Fritillaria Imperialis* or crown imperial grows from 3' to 4' high. The yellow or bronze flowers which have a checkered pattern on the outside, grow forming in terminal umbels. The fact that so many species are checkered (*Fritillus,* Dice-Box) fritillary the name of checkered lily *(B)*.

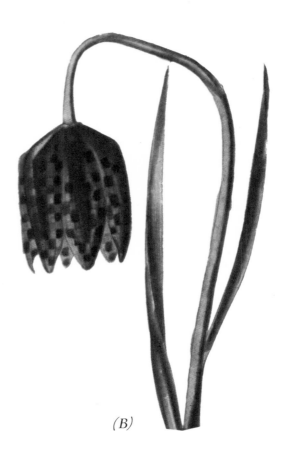

(B)

(A)

Fumaria

Fumatory

There are about twenty species, mostly annual herbs, in this genus. *Fumaria Officinalis,* common fumatory or fume of the earth, is an annual growing between 8" and 32" high with a tender brittle stem. The flowers are violet-purple and in loose terminal clusters. As its name suggests, it gives off a very unpleasant odor when crushed and it has a bitter disagreeable taste. Once much used in medicine, it is still regarded as effective in treating skin diseases *(A)*.

Galanthus Nivalis

Common Snowdrop

The flowers are about 1" long with green streaked inner segments within. There are usually two leaves which are linear, wide, glaucous and keeled. The plant grows between 3" and 8" high and is found from France east to the Caucusus. It is sometimes called fair maid of February since it flowers in that month *(B)*.

Gallium

Bedstraw

There are about 220 species of these mostly weedy plants. *Galium Verum,* yellow or lady's bedstraw was used to curdle milk for cheesemaking. It is a climbing plant that holds for dear life onto neighboring plants, attaching itself by little hooks on its stem and leaves *(C)*.

(B)   *(C)*

(A)

Gentiana

Gentian

Yellow gentian or *Gentiana Lutea* is an erect unbranched perennial, 4' to 6' high. The flowers are more or less whorled in shape and pale yellow veined or spotted in color. It furnishes the commercial gentian root. The name comes from Gentius, King of Illyria, who is said to have been the first to experience the virtues of Gentian. Purple-flowered gentian or *Gentiana Purpurea* is a perennial growing 1' to 2' high. *Gnetiana Pneumonanthe,* calathian violet or marsh gentian is a perennial with deep purple to purple-blue flowers, and it grows 6" to 12" high. The most common species in the United States is *Gentiana Andrewsii* (Catesbaei) which has deep blue flowers growing both in terminal flower heads and in the upper axils; they are white on the lobes. *(A).*

Geum

Avens

There are about thirty-six species in this genus. The yellow, red or white flowers grow solitary or in loose panicles. The leaves are variously cut. They are native to cold and temperate regions and make excellent border and rock plants. The roots of some species have the same qualities as Peruvian bark *(Cinchona) (B).*

(B)   *(A)*

(A)

Glaucium

Horned Poppy

There are about twelve species of glaucous, annual, biennial or perennial herbs. The flowers are large and solitary, yellow or crimson. *Glaucium Flavum* grows 1' to 2' high with radical leaves which are many-stalked, pinnatifid and hairy. The flowers are large and bright yellow.

Glechoma
Ground Ivy

This plant has a creeping stem, often several feet long. The leaves are kidney-shaped, roughly 1" across, crenate and stalked. The flowers are blue or yellow— and grow in axillary whorls of about six *(A)*.

Helichrysum
Everlasting Flower

There are about 300 species native to the warm and temperate regions of the Old World. The flower heads vary from solitary to clustered and the colors, white, pink, cream, golden or straw yellow, are bright beautiful and very long-lasting. The greatest concentration of these plants is in South Africa and Australia *(B)*.

(B)   *(A)*

Hepatica Triloba
Noble Liverwort

Noble Liverwort or Liver Leaf, is found in the north temperate zone, including North America. The leaves are cordate, three-lobed, occasionally toothed and obtuse. The flowers—blue white or pink—grow on silky, downy stems 4" to 6" high. Despite its name, there is no evidence that it was ever used for liver disorders. In America, however, it was used to treat lung diseases *(A)*.

Humulus Lupulus
Bine

Bine or common Hop has a rough angled stem. The leaves are cordate, toothed and rough. The flowers are greenish-yellow, the males grow in loose axillary panicles, the females in short-stalked axillary roundish spikes. The fruit is a sort of cone with ovoid achenes surrounded by yellow resinous bitter granules; the fruit heads are used in brewing, and the young blanched shoots are used as a pot-herb *(B)*.

(B)

(B)

(A)

Hypericum

St John's Wort

This is the Yterikon of Dioscorides. The genus includes shrubs, subshrubs and herbs, varying in size according to the species. The most common type, found in dry places particularly on the edge of woods, grows between 12" and 30" high. The stems are cylindrical and the leaves are oval, opposite, contain pellucid glands and are dark green in color. The flowers are yellow and perfect. One of the most beautiful and hardiest species is *Hypericum Calcynimum,* rose of sharon or Aaron's beard *(A).*

Juniperus

Juniper

Common juniper is either a low spreading or tall erect bush according to its environment. The flowers are axillary and solitary, reduced to the sexual organs. The fruit is black with a glaucous bloom when ripe. It contains an aromatic pulp, bitter-sweet in taste, said to help the digestion. In good conditions, this tree can grow to 15' or higher. It is gound wild in chalky soils *(B).*

(A)

(B)

Lavendula
Lavander

This is a genus of about twenty species of shrubs, sub-shrubs and perennial herbs. The leaves are opposite, entire or toothed. The flowers are blue or violet, and grow crowded in cylindrical spikes, 1" to 3" long, at the top of slender peduncles, 1' to 2' high, in whorls of up to ten. Common lavander or *Lavandula Spica* and *Lavandula vera* are highly valued for cutting and drying because of their exquisite fragrance. They are used in the preparation of essential oil, and for scenting bed linen and cupboards *(A)*.

Linaria
Toad Flax

Common toad flax is an erect perennial 2' to 3' high. Its leaves are either linear or linear-lance-shaped; the flowers are pale yellow or citron with a copper-colored palate, and the spur is curved as long as the corolla forming spike-like, dense racemes *(B)*.

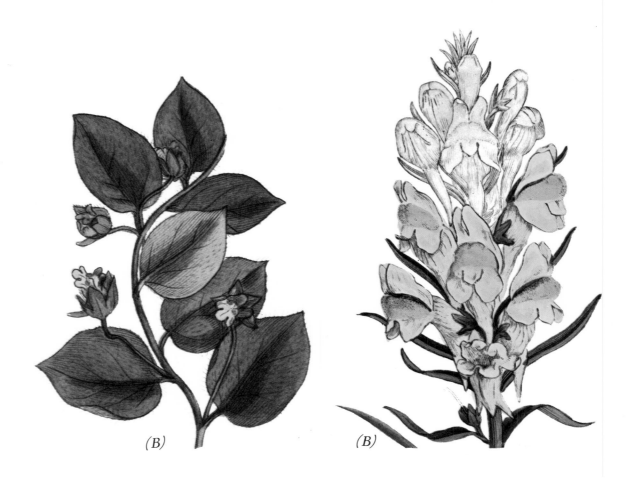

(B)   (B)

Linum
Flax

    This is genus of about ninety species, usually glabrous annual, of biennial or perennial herbs or shrubs. *Linum usitatissimum* or common and flax is an annual about 18" high, with an erect stem, blue flowers growing in corymbose panicles, and linear or lance-shaped leaves. Certain varieties are used to supply the fibers for making linen and the oil of their seeds (known as linseed) is used by artists for mixing their oil paints *(A)*.

Lolium Perenne
Rye Grass

    The stems are either solitary or few, between 2' and 3' high, and bear alternate leaves. The greenish flowers are inconspicuous and grow clustered in alternate spikelets which together make one spike on the upper part of the stem. It is very common in sandy fields and on uncultivated land. During the harvest it is essential to separate the chaff from the wheat in order to prevent it from getting mixed in with the wheat flour where it can be fatal if eaten *(B)*.

Lonicera
Honeysuckle

    Named after Adam Lonitzer (1528-86) a German botanist and physician, this genus includes 180 species. *Lonicera Periclymenum,* honeysuckle or woodbine, is a deciduous climbing shrub, 10' to 20' high, growing over bushes in the wild state. The leaves are ovate, oval or obovate; the flowers are stalkless, borne in 3 to 5 close whorls, and form a terminal stalked fragrant inflorescence. The corolla is yellowish-white suffused with yellowish-purple. The fruit is globose red, closely clustered. *Lonicera Flava,* one very rare beautiful species with bright orange-yellow flowers is found in the southeastern United States *(C)*.

(B)

(C)

(A)

Lotus
Bird's Foot Trefoil

This is a member of the *Leguminosæ.* The name comes from the way in which the leaves are cut. *Lotus corniculatus* is a procumbent perennial with obovate, acute, and entire leaflets. The flowers are bright yellow fading to orange; the common cultivated type has flowers which are striped red at the base in front growing on long flower stalks. Wild, it is found in uncultivated fields or growing among wheat and corn *(A)*.

Lychnis Flos Cuculi
Cuckooflower

Cuckooflower or ragged robin has a thick rootstock, stems from 12" to 24" high, which are usually hairy and flushed red near the nodes. The flowers are rose, occasionally white, although there is a cultivated variety, *albiflora*, which has white flowers. The variety known as *pleniflora* is a double flowered species. They grow near the waterside *(B)*.

(B)

(A)

Lysimachia

Creeping Jenny

Creeping Jenny or moneybags is a prostrate glabrose perennial with a stem one-foot long or more; its leaves are opposite, roundish, obtuse and short-stalked. The flowers are bright yellow, solitary, and grow in the leaf axils. It was believed by the ancients to be fatal for flies and snakes *(A)*.

Lythrum Salicaria

Purple Loosestrife

This is an herbaceous perennial, 2' to 5' high, with leaves which are either opposite or whorled, and always lance-shaped; the red-purple flowers grow in axillary clusters forming a terminal spike-like raceme. They do best on the banks of streams. They have been used in the past to make a decoction for cases of dysentery *(B)*.

(A)

(B)

Malva
Mallow

    Malva Sylvestris is an erect little-branched perennial about 18" high. The leaves have 5 to 7 lobers are toothed and veined with dark pink or violet flowers. The flowers are quite large, purple in color with streaks of violet and, sometimes, although rarely, blue.

Melampyrum
Cow-wheat

The name is derived from the Greek word *melas* meaning black and *pyros* meaning wheat; the seeds are like dark grains of wheat. *Melampyrum arvense* or Purple Cow-wheat is a plant 1' to 2' high, with a stout stem which is four-angled, erect, branched and rough. The leaves are lance-shaped and entire although the upper leaves are toothed at the base. The flowers are rose-red, curved and downy with a yellow throat and a deep pink lip; many flowers grow in bracteate spikes (the bracts are rosy-purple and leafy). Its seeds can be used to make a violet-red bread, but usually this plant is destroyed *(A)*.

Mentha
Mint

There are about forty species of aromatic perennial herbs in this genus. *Mentha piperita* is peppermint, a plant with a running rootstock, a glabrous stem 1' to 2' high which is branched and reddish in color. The leaves are ovate-oblong, acute, toothed and occasionally hairy on the veins beneath. The flowers are purple and grow in short, loose, blunt terminal spikes *(B)*.

(A)   *(B)*

Myrrhis Odorata

Myrrh

Anise, myrrh or sweet cicely is a perennial with very fine hairs. The root is fleshy and carrot-like, the stem which is 2' to 3' high is leafy, hollow, grooved and branched above. The leaves are thrice-pinnate, and whitish in color beneath. The flowers are small and white—only the outer flowers are fertile in the umbel, the inner staminate. When mixed with other leaves, the plant and its seeds were once used as a salad; the roots when boiled could also be used as a salad *(A)*.

Narcissus

Daffodil

The daffodil, found wild in woods and fields, is one of the first plants to flower in spring. The stem is erect and angular, bearing only a single yellow flower. The leaves are sword-shaped and are not as long as the stem. *Narcissus poeticus,* pheasant's eye, has many varieties. Generally the scape is about 12" long, bearing a solitary fragrant flower, with a cylindrical tube; the segments are spreading, broad and obovate. The color is pure white tinged with yellow at the base *(B)*.

(A)

(B)

(B)

Nepeta

Catmint

There are about 150 species in this genus all found in the extra-tropical regions of the northern hemisphere. The leaves are opposite and the flowers which grow in axillary whorls or in spikes are usually blue or white and occasionally yellow. *Nepeta Cataria,* catnip or catmint, is an erect, hoary herb 2' to 3' high. The flowers are white and the corolla is dotted with purple. The infused leaves were once used as a home remedy *(A)*.

Onobrychis Viciifolia

Saintfoin

Saintfoin, Fodder Grass or Hen's Bill is an erect plant 2' to 3' high. The leaflets are elliptical-oblong and mucronate; the flowers are variegated and grow on long spikes. The name comes from the Greek word *onos* meaning ass and *brycho* meaning to bray, since it was considered the favorite food of donkeys *(B)*.

(A)

(B)

Ononis

Rest-Harrow

Onosis arvensis, spinosa or *procurrens,* Cammock or Rest-harrow, flowers between May and August and grows to between 1' and 2 1/4' high.   The stems are glandular-hairy, the flowers are regular, large and solitary, growing from the leaf axils on the upper part of the stems and forming loose terminal racemes.   The corolla is usually rosy-pink or pink and white.   The plant is often spiny and it is said that you may lose your finger if your are pricked by it. *(A).*

Ophrys

Ophrys

This belongs to the orchid family and is found particularly in Mediterranean regions. *Ophrys apifera,* or Bee Orchid has a stem 9" to 18" high, oblong leaves and pretty flowers clustered in loose spikes.   The perianth segments are usually pink—in contrasting to the globular, velvety, red-brown lip—with a variable yellow pattern, resembling the thorax of a bee.   It grows along hedgerows and at the edge of woods *(B).*

(B)

(A)

Orchis
Orchid

Flowers in this genus have 4 equal perianth segments, often forming a "helmet", and a conspicuous lip which is usually 3- or 4-lobed. *Orchis mascula* or early purple orchid has an oval or cylindrical cluster consisting of many flowers which are dark crimson-purple and smell like tomcats. The tubers of this and other orchids produce a starch-like substance called bassorine; an ounce a day is said to be enough to sustain a man. *(A)*.

Papaver Rhoeas
Corn Poppy

This is an annual erect, branched plant 1' to 2 1/2' high, with spreading bristly hairs. Leaves can be up to 6" long. The flowers grow on long peduncles, clothed with spreading hairs; they are brilliant scarlet with a black basal blotch. Cultivated varieties have been developed from one form of the species which has white-edged petals. A number of colors are now available, except yellow, including double forms *(B)*.

(A)   *(B)*

(B)

Passiflora

Passion Flower

There are over 300 species in this genus of herbaceous and woody climbers. The stems are frequently angular, the leaves are alternate and variable in shape, the flowers are mostly solitary and grow in leaf axils, sometimes in pairs. One beautiful species is *Passiflora racemosa* with flowers which grow in terminal racemes, rosy-crimson sepals and petals similar in color; the outer rays are purple with white tips and the inner very short and red. The species vary so greatly while that are used in Brazil to make refreshing drinks; one variety, common in the Antilles, is poisonous *(A)*.

Petasites

Butterburr

This is a genus of fourteen species usually consisting of large perennial herbs related to Tussilago and Senecio. One pot-grown species *Petasites fragrans* is particularly welcome in winter for its pretty flowers *(B)*.

Pimpinella

Anise

This genus covers about seventy species of perennial, although occasionally annual, herbs found in the north temperate regions (North Africa and South America). The leaves are pinnate or ternate; the umbel is compound and consists of white or yellow flowers. *Pimpinella Anisum* is the hardy aniseed plant. This is a branched annual, about 18" high; the leaves are radical and lobed; the flowers are yellowish-white growing in loose compound umbels; the fruit is greenish-grey, oblong, furrowed, aromatic, sweet and spicy. Sources differ as to whether the plant comes from Greece or originated in Egypt *(C)*.

(A)

(B)

(C)

Plantago
Plantain

Plantain or *waybread* covers about 260 species, mostly herbs. The leaves are usually radical and alternate; the flowers are small and inconspicuous and grow either in short globose heads or elongated spikes—they are either bisexual or unisexual on the same plant. Scientists such as Dioscorides recommended a decoction of this plant as a remedy for eye diseases. The gum produced from its seeds can be used to prepare a hair-setting lotion *(A)*.

Potentilla
Cinquefoil

The name *potentilla* means powerful and is applied to this herb because of its reputed medicinal qualities. *Potentilla villosa* is a silky-hairy perennial herb 4" to 12" high; the flowers are pink up to 1" across, and grow in few-flowered clusters. It is native to the western regions of North America. *Potentilla Anserina,* which has showy yellow flowers, is silverweed or argentine, and is sought after for the tannin in its leaves *(B)*.

(A)

(B)

Primula Veris
Cowslip

The flowers of this plant are deep yellow, fragrant, concave with the obcordate lobes; the scape 3" to 8" long, is downy; the leaves are ovate or ovate-lance-shaped, the margin is crimped with white hairs beneath. The leaves can be eaten as a salad or mixed with honey to make a pleasant drink. The stems are eaten in Sumatra to ward off scurvy *(A)*.

Prunella
Self-heal

Prunella or brunella is a herb which is supposed to heal a disease of the jaws and to cure quinsy. There are about twelve species. The leaves are entire, deeply toothed or pinnatifid; the flowers are purplish, bluish or white. *Prunella vulgaris,* allheal or selfheal has prostrate stems 4" to 12" long, occasionally ascending to about 3" in height; the leaves are ovate-oblong or oblong-lance-shaped, either entire or toothed and often purplish in color. The lower leaves are stalked, the upper are sessile. The flowers are purple, occasionally pink or white, and the calyx is purple as well *(B)*.

Prunus
Blackthorn

This is a densely branched spiny bush 8' to 10' high. The flowers are white and solitary, usually, with small pedicels. The fruit is round, blue-black and waxy. The wood, being hard, is often used for rake teeth. The leaves, flowers and even the bark can be distilled and yield an oil having similar characteristics to those of bitter almond. When fermented the fruits make a pleasant liqueur *(C)*.

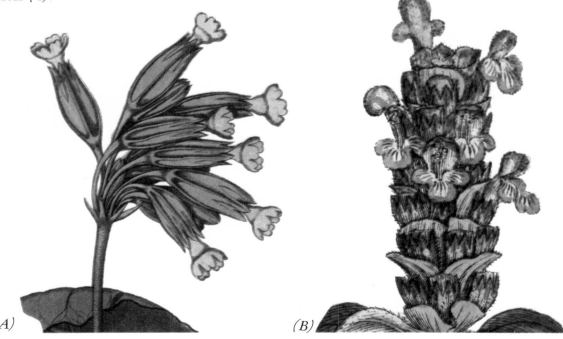

(A)

(B)

(C)

Ranunculus
Buttercup

Ranunculus acris or the common buttercup, is a hairy plant growing 8" to 3' high. The lower leaves are stalked 3- to 7- partite, the segments deeply cut and lobed; the upper leaves are sessile with the segments being linear and entire. The flowers are yellow, about 1" across. It is also known as blister plant, gold knots or meadow ranunculus. Yellow batchelor's buttons is the double-flowered variety. The great red-flowered single form, found wild in the Levant, is most striking and may perhaps be the "lily of the field" mentioned in Matthew 7:28 *(A)*.

Rhamnus
Buckthorn

This genus about consists of 100 species, mostly small trees and shrubs. The flowers are tiny and green. Common buckthorn or *Rhamus cathartica* is a deciduous shrub 10' to 20' high. The leaves are opposite and alternate on the same shoot, either oval or ovate and finely toothed; the small green flowers are borne in the lower leaf axils in crowded clusters. The fruit is black and globose—it is violently purgative. The North American species *Rhamnus Purshiana* or cascara sagrada grows between 35' and 45' high and its bark yields the drug cascara. One of the most handsome and longest-leaved buckthorns is *Rahmnus imeritina* which turns bronze-purple in the autumn *(B)*.

Rheum
Rhubarb

There are about twenty species of these stout perennial herbs. *Rheum Rhaponticum* or common rhubarb grows about 4' high. Its leaves are roundish in outline, deeply cordate at the base, undulate, glabrous above, and downy beneath and on the veins; the flowers grow in dense leafy fastigiate panicles. It has remarkable purgative properties and makes very good jam. It has been used particularly in China for making elixirs to prolong life. Homeopaths regard it as a tonic *(C)*.

Rhinanthus
Yellow Rattle

This is an annual plant, a parasite in fact. It has a erect stem 15" to 2' high. The flowers are fairly large, yellow, short-stalked, and grow in leafy terminal clusters. When dried this plant becomes quite black *(D)*.

(A)

(B)

(C)

(D)

Rhododendron

These are shrubs or trees with alternate, simple entire leaves, whose flowers grow in clusters, which are mostly terminal, but sometimes axillary or solitary; the corolla is generally bell- or funnel-shapped. *Rhododendron chrysanthum* is a dwarf evergreen, usually under 1' in height. Its flowers are yellow, akin to and resembling *Rhododendron caucasicum.* It is very rare and difficult to cultivate. Two American species *Rhododendron canadense* and *carolinianum* have rose-purple flowers, the latter being rather paler.

Robinia

False Acacia

The name *Robinia* comes from the French botanist, Robin. There are about twenty species of deciduous trees and shrubs. The leaves are alternate and unequally pinnate; the flowers, growing in pendulous racemes, are often fragrant. *Robinia hispida* or rose acacia comes from the south eastern United States and grows from 5' to 6' high with clusters of 5-10 flowers growing in pendant racemes. They are deep rose in color. One variety of this species, called *macrophylla,* has the most beautiful flowers of the entire genus—larger and more richly colored. *Robinia Pseudacacia* is the locuts or acacia, with fragrant white flowers arranged on pendulous racemes, 4"-7" long. The petals are blotched yellow at the base. There are many variable forms prepared from seed *(A)*.

Rosa Canina

Dog Rose

The dog rose grows 6'-10' high, with long and arching branches; the flowers are white to deep pink, solitary or clustered. The scarlet fruit's shape is ovoid to slightly globose. The China rose or monthly rose grows between 4' and 20' high and has brown, hooked thorns. The flowers are crimson to pink or almost white, and the fruit is scarlet. The Damask rose has flowers varying from white to red, which grow in large fragrant corymbs. Sweetbriar, and eglantine, the single yellow rose, are members of the same family *(B)*.

(A)   *(B)*

(B)

Rosmarinus
Rosemary

Rosemary is a maritime plant sometimes called seadew. *Rosmarinus officinalis* is a hardy evergreen shrub used for making rosemary tea which is said to relieve headaches. It has also been used to make rosemary wine, and the young fresh leaves, stems and flowers are used to flavor stews and sauces, cider cups, claret cups and salads. It can grow up to 7' high, but is usually much shorter. The few flowers are pale violet *(A)*.

Rubus
Bramble, Raspberry

There are about 500 species in this genus. The leaves are alternate, simple, digitate or pinnate. The flowers are white or pink. The wild raspberry is known as *Rubus idæus*. The best blackberries are obtained from *Rubus schlechtendalii. Rubus canadensis* is pretty in blossom *(B)*.

Sagittaria
Arrowhead

There are about thirty species of these herbs which are mainly waterside plants. *Sagittaria sagittifolia* or common arrowhead is stononiferous, with a swollen rootstock. The spear-shaped leaves are either acute or obtuse, and the stalks are stout; the flowers are about 1/2" across (the male is larger) and the petals have purple claws. *Sagittaria latifolia,* duck potato or wapato, is found in North America *(C)*.

(C)

(A)

(B)

Salvia
Sage

Common sage or *Salvia officinalis* is a shrub about 1' high, with a nearly white and wooly stem; the flowers are purple, blue or white and form 10-20 flowered whorls in a raceme. Culinary sage is mostly used as stuffing for which the narrow-leaved form with white flowers is said to be the best. In the pleasure garden, the purple-leaved form is preferred, along with *Salvia splendens* or scarlet sage which comes from Brazil and has scarlet flowers in spike-like racemes. Meadow sage or *Salvia pratensis* is a perennial about 2' high with bright blue flowers growing in spikes of up to 18" high *(A)*.

Sanguisorba Minor
Burnet

This plant grows from 1' to 2 1/2' high, and is sometimes slightly hairy. The leaves are long; the flowers have terminal small heads—the lower flowers are bisexual or staminate and upper are female. The leaves are sometimes used in soup and with borage in salads *(B)*.

(B)

(A)

Sambucus Nigra
Elder

The elder tree is in fact a shrub or a tree growing up to 30'. The flowers are yellowish or dull white growing flat cymes, with a heavy odor. The fruit is generally shining black, but there are many varieties. The fruit is used to make elderberry wine, and has laxative properties. The bark is rich in sugar, gum, salts, acids and various other substances *(A)*.

Saxifraga
Rockfoil

These are mostly perennial herbs with white or yellow flowers. *Saxifraga granulata* is known as Meadow Saxifrage or "fair maids of France". It is a deciduous tufted plant with kidney-shaped leaves and bulbils at the base of the stem. The stem grows to about 12" tall with large white flowers, growing in loose panicles *(B)*.

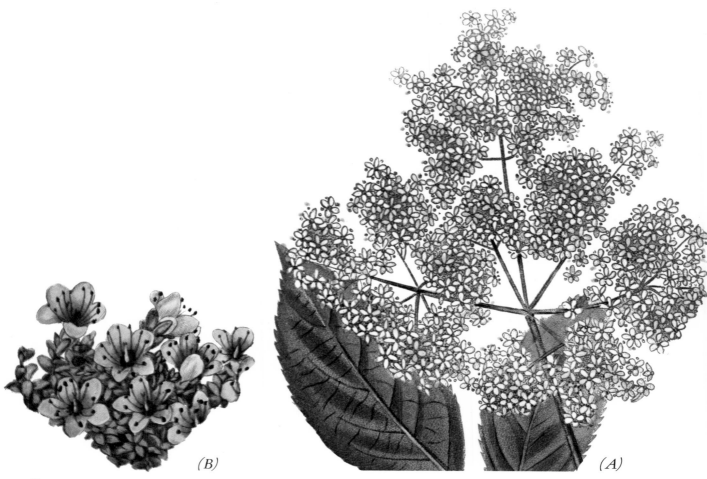

(B)

(A)

(A)

Scilla

Squill

    Scilla amoena or nodding squill has blue flowers, sometimes whitish, and is found in woods and shady fields. Wild hyacinth or *Scilla nonscripta* is a hardy plant with blue flowers, sometimes white or pink, growing in drooping racemes. Sea squill, *Urginea maritima,* has flower spikes with numerous white flowers forming a cylindrical cluster on a leafless unbranched stem; it blooms in autumn. The leaves appear later. The bulbs have been used since classical times for medicinal purposes; when eaten in quantity these are poisonous. A related North African species is the source of red squill rat poison *(A)*.

Sedum

Stonecrop

    There are about 300 species of these glabrous, glandular-hairy, fleshy erect or recumbent herbs. The name comes from the Latin for "to sit;" they are therefore good rockplants. *Sedum acre,* stonecrop or wallpepper is a creeping, mat-forming, glabrous evergreen with barren shoots. The flowers are yellow and numerous. It is known by many names such as "prick madam," "jack of the buttery", "love entangled" (North Ohio) and "treasure of love"(Boston) *(B)*.

(A)   *(B)*

(B)

Sempervivum Tectorum
House Leek

Common Houseleek or St Patrick's cabbage has rosettes 2" to 3" across, open and flattish. The leaves are green, red or white at the base, usually large with a purple tip and very fleshy. The flowers with 12 to 16 parts are dark or light purplish-red about 1" across. The stems 8" to 12" long with white shaggy hairs. There are many varieties *(A)*.

Sinapis
Mustard

There are about eight species of these annual, hairy herbs found mainly in the Mediterranean region. *Sinapis arvensis* or charlock is an erect branched hairy annual 10" to 24" high. The flowers are yellow growing in racemes containing 35 to 50 flowers. The seeds are a dark reddish-brown, about 8 to 13 in a fruit, with a deciduous two-edged conical or awl-shaped beak. In its wild state it is found in grassy places or on the banks of streams. In the garden it is a persistent weed *(B)*.

Sinapis Arvensis
Black Mustard

This annual plant has a robust harly stem bearing petiolate leaves, that may grow up to 3' high. The flowers of wild mustard or charlack are yellow, containing a calyx with four spreading sepals. The fruit contains brownish-black seeds that are used to make the condiment mustard and the irritant mustard oil. It is a valuable fodder crop *(C)*.

(A)

(C)

(B)

Spartium
Spanish Broom

Spartium junceum is a rather gaunt shrub growing up to 10' high with nearly erect branches and reed-like shoots. The leaves are very sparse; the flowers are fragrant and grow in loose terminal racemes; the corolla is large and shining yellow. Also known as rush broom this plant produces material for making paper *(A)*.

Spiræa Ulmaria
Meadowsweet

Meadowsweet or "Queen of the Meadows" has regulard flowers, usually hermaphrodite, growing in clusters or cymes. Common meadowsweet has a tufted white inflorescence. Most species have small white, pink or carmine flowers. *Spiræa prunifolia plena* is a beautiful species bearing pure wreath-like white flowers on twigs 1' to 2' long. Its autumn foliage is red *(B)*.

(A)

(B)

(B)

Taraxacum Vulgare
Dandelion

There are about sixty species in this genus. *Taraxacum officinale* reproduces by parthenogenesis reproduction. It has a long, stout root, radical leaves which are oblong-ovate to spatulate and variously cut. The flower heads are bright yellow while the outer rays are often brown at the back. It has considerable medical value especially in the roots of the wild plants, and the blanched leaves can be used as salad *(A)*.

Thalictrum
Meadow Rue

This genus contains about 130 species with small flowers green, yellow or mauve in color. Common meadow rue or "poor man's rhubarb" is a perennial with yellow, pinkish or even white flowers, without a corolla, growing in terminal clusters which together form one large panicle. Found in damp fields, at the waterside and in wood clearings, its flowers have long been used to make potions against the common cold *(B)*.

Thlaspi
Pennycress

These are annual or perennial herbs with white, purple or pale-purple flowers growing in racemes. A related plant, *Capsella* or shepherd's purse, is a common annual herb found almost all the year round in cultivated land or on old walls. The flowers are white, pink or yellowish. *(C)*.

(B)   *(C)*   *(A)*

(A)

Thymus

Thyme

    Thymus vulgaris, garden or common thyme, is a spreading bush 6" to 8" high; the leaves are oblong-lance-shaped to linear; the flowers are pink, sometimes white, and grow in tiny axillary tufts together forming leafy terminal clusters. It has properties for stimulating the whole organism *(A)*.

Thymus Serpyllum

Creeping Thyme

    Mother of thyme, wild or creeping thyme, is a mat-forming plant. The leaves are narrowly elliptic to narrowly obovate, short-stalked, blunt and gland-dotted. The inflorescence is hemispherical and the calyx and corolla are purplish. It has a taste similar to common thyme, although not as strong, and has similar properties. According to Linnaeus, the renowned Swedish botanist, it is capable of dispelling drunkenness *(B)*.

(B)

(A)

(A)

(B)

Tilia
Lime Tree

There are about thirty species of these large to medium trees. *Tilia europea* or common lime has glabrous shoots, and yellowish-white fragrant flowers growing in pendant cymes of 5 to 10 flowers a piece. The leaves are broadly ovate and obliquely cordate. The inner bark of this species is tough and fibrous and is used to make bast mats to cover glass frames in cold weather; peasants use it in Russia to make shoes. The American lime is a species which grows up to 130'. *(A)*.

Trifolium
Clover

There are about 300 species of these annual, biennial or perennial herbs, all native to the northern hemisphere. *Trifolium repens,* the white clover or shamrock, grows about 3" high, *purpureum* or the four-leaved shamrock is the one considered to bring good luck. *Hibernicum* is the shamrock of Ireland. Clovers make excellent cattle forage since they have nitrogen-fixing properties *(B)*.

Ulex
Gorse

Ulex europeus is a densely spiny shrub, which grows 2' to 4' high in the wild and twice as high in cultivated gardens. The flowers are golden-yellow. In Celtic regions it is used for hedgerows and enclosures. In poor areas it is the main fodder for cows *(C)*.

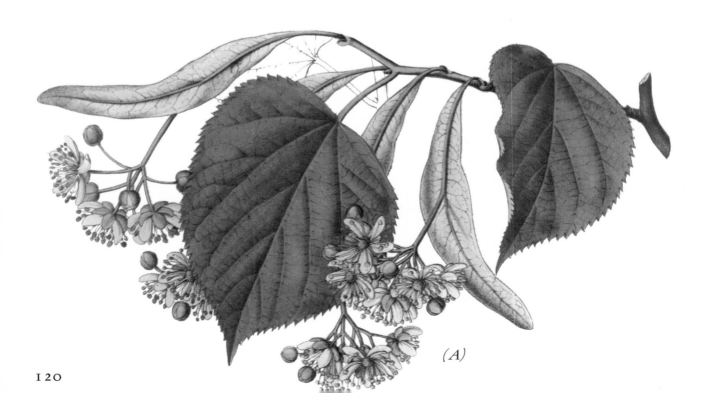

(A)

(B)

(C)

Urtica

Nettle

The stinging nettles are: *Urtica urens,* the small nettle, an annual with pale green and saw-toothed leaves; *Urtica dioica* or the common nettle is a perennial which is slightly larger and has duller green leaves. *Urtica urentissima,* a native of Timor is so virulent that the effects last for months and may even cause death. The perennial when young can replace spinach. It yields a strong fiber useful for weaving fine textiles *(A).*

Valeriana

Valerian

Valeriana officinalis, all-heal, cat's valerian or common valerian is a perennial herb about 3' high with sulcate stems, and pinnatisect leaves; the pink flowers grow in a corymb. Cats love this plant, especially the powdered root. It is found in sandy places *(B).*

(B)   *(A)*

(A)

Verbascum Thapsus

Aaron's Rod

This is a densely woolly plant with an unbranched, stout stem 2' to 3' high; the basal leaves are obovate and lance-shaped, the stem leaves are oblong and acute; the flowers are yellow and grow in a single spike 6" to 10" long. Also known as cow's or lung wort it is one of the "pectoral" flowers. Its wool was once used to make lampwicks *(A)*.

Veronica

Speedwell

There are about 250 species of these small trees, shrubs, annual or perennial herbs all found in the cooler parts of the northern hemisphere. *Veronica agrestis* or procumbent speedwell is an annual weed with small light-blue or pinkish flowers. *Veronica arvensis* or wall speedwell has whitish flowers growing in a terminal raceme. *Veronica americana* or American brookline is a perennial with small violet or lilac flowers. For a long time, the European species was used in Germany to replace tea. It is a stimulant and a diuretic *(B)*.

Vicia

Vetch

This genus covers about 120 species of annual or perennial herbs. The leaves are equally pinnate, the leaflets are usually numerous and the leaf often ends in a tendril. The flowers are papilonaceous (resembling the shape of a butter-fly), often blue-violet, yellowish-white or white, and grow in an axillary raceme. *Vicia faba* is known as the broad bean. *Vicia villosa,* winter of hairy vetch is found in granite-bearing ground and withstands the cold better than most *(C)*.

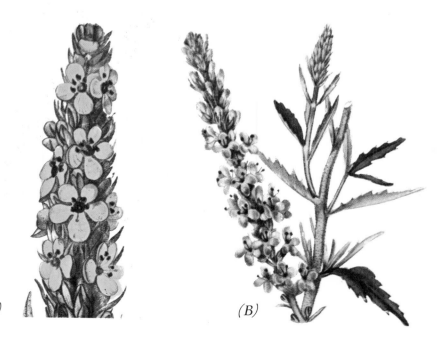

(A)   *(B)*

(C)

Vinca

Periwinkle

There are about ten species of these erect or procumbent herbs or sub-shrubs. In the wild their flowers are blue, sometimes violet or white. *Vinca major,* band plant or cut finger has tough stems with ovate and ciliate leaves; the flowers are bluish-purple *(A)*.

Viscum

Mistletoe

There are about seventy species of these shrubs (parasitic when growing on trees). *Viscum album* or common mistletoe is an evergreen unisexual shrub, tawny or yellowish in color, which is usually attached to the host in the form of a pendulous dichotomously branched bush 2' to 3' wide. The flowers are inconspicuous, sessile, and grow in the forks or the branches. The fruit is translucent, white, globose, with one seed embedded in the pulp. Once used for the mysterious rites of the Druids, it is now best known for the part it plays at Christmas. (See p. 128.)

(A)

(A)

(B)